The Moon Monsters Get Lost

Some moon monsters were going on a trip.

We are lost! Check the map!

Go left at the moon.

But they got lost.

They went right at the moon.

The moon monsters went too far.

They had no oil ...

... they had to land in Marla's garden.

This is Marla.

The next morning, Marla got up.

She went out to the garden.

Wow! There are moon monsters in my garden!

Marla went to tell her mum and dad.

What?

Come and see!

Moon monsters?

They went out to the garden to look at the moon monsters.

Dad did not like
the moon monsters!

Eek! Moon monsters!
Do not splat me!
I do not wish to hurt you!

The moon monsters were sad that they were stuck.

Boo hoo!
We are stuck!

The star ship needs oil!

Marla's dad had some oil.

You can have my oil.

The moon monsters got back into the star ship ...

Thanks!

... and went back to the moon.

Off you go, moon monsters!